CW00409261

Exclusive Distributors

International Music Publications Limited
Griffin House, 161 Hammersmith Road, London W6 8BS, England

International Music Publications GmbH, Germany
Marstallstraße 8, D-80539 Munchen, Germany

Nuova Carisch S.p.a.
Italy: Nuova Carisch Srl, Via Campania 12
20098 San Giuliano Milanese, Milano

France: Carisch Musicom
25 Rue d'Hauteville, 75010 Paris

Spain: Nueva Carisch España
Magallanes 25, 28015 Madrid

www.carisch.com

Danmusik
Vognmagergade 7, DK-1120 kobenhavn, Denmark

Warner/Chappell Music Australia Pty Ltd.
3 Talavera Road, North Ryde, New South Wales 2113, Australia

Folio © 2000 International Music Publications Ltd
Griffin House, 161 Hammersmith Road, London W6 8BS, England

Printed by The Panda Group, Haverhill,Suffolk CB9 8PRI, UK
Binding by Haverhill Print Finishers

Photo Pages: Paul M Smith

Let Love Be Your Energy

Out of a million seeds
Only the strongest one breathes
You made a miracle mother
I'll make a man out of me

Daddy where's the sun gone from the sky?
What did we do wrong, why did it die?
And all the grown ups say 'sorry kids we got no reply'

If you're willing to change the world
Let love be your energy
I've got more than I need
When your love shines down on me

Every tear that you cry
Will be replaced when you die
Why don't you love your brother?
Are you out of your mind?

Daddy where's the sun gone from the sky
What did we do wrong, why did it die
And if you've got no love for me then I'll say goodbye

If you're willing to change the world
Let love be your energy
I've got more than I need
When your love shines down on me

If you're willing to change the world
Let love be your energy
I can't contain how I feel
When your love shines down on me
Well if you want it come and make a stance
So when it's in your hands
People show me love

Well if you want it come and make a stance
So when it's in your hands
People show me love

If you're willing to change the world
Let love be your energy
I got more than I need
When your love shines down on me

If you're willing to change the world
Let love be your energy
I can't contain how I feel
When your love shines down on me

Rock DJ

Me with the floorshow
Kickin' with your torso
Boys getting high
And the girls even more so
Wave your hands if you're not with the man
Can I kick it (yes you can)
I got (funk)
You got (soul)
We got everybody
I've got the gift
Gonna stick it in the goal
It's time to move your body

Babylon back in business
Can I get a witness
Every girl every man
Houston do you hear me
Ground-control can you feel me
Need permission to land
I don't wanna rock, DJ
But you're making me feel so nice
When's it gonna stop, DJ
'Cause you're keepin' me up all night

Singin' in the classes
Music for your masses
Give no head
No backstage passes
Have a proper giggle
I'll be quite polite
But when I rock the mike
I rock the mike (right)
You got no love then you're with the wrong man
It's time to move your body
If you can't get a girl but your best friend can
It's time to move your body

I don't wanna be sleazy
Baby just tease me
Got no family planned
Houston do you hear me
Ground-control can you feel me
Need permission to land
I don't wanna rock, DJ
But you're making me feel so nice
When's it gonna stop, DJ
'Cause you're keepin' me up all night

I don't wanna rock, DJ
But you're making me feel so nice
When's it gonna stop, DJ
'Cause you're keepin' me up all night

Pimpin' ain't easy
Most of them fleece me
Every night
Pimpin' ain't easy
But if you're sellin' it
It's alright

Come on
I don't wanna rock, DJ
But you're making me feel so nice
When's it gonna stop DJ
'Cause you're keepin' me up all night

I don't wanna rock, DJ
But you're making me feel so nice
When's it gonna stop, DJ
'Cause you're keepin' me up all night

Singing For The Lonely

Singing for the lonely
You're not the only ones who feel this
So scared of what we're doing
All the time

Here comes wasted head-space
Paranoia
Anger, misplaced feelings
Leave me nowhere
All the time

I don't wake up early every morning
'Cause the more I sleep the less I have to say
Scared of you always thinking that I'm boring
Stop me yawning my life away

Tender young confusion
Send black mariah for blue delusions
Lays heavy oh so heavy
On my mind

I'm so sick of people's expectations
Leaves me tired all the time
If your home's full of useless aggravation
Then don't bring it to mine

I seem to spend my life
Just waiting for the chorus
'Cause the verse is never nearly
Good enough

The hooligan half of me
That steals from Woolworths
While the other lives for love

I'm so sick of people's expectations
Leaves me tired all the time
If your home's full of worthless aggravation
Then don't bring it to mine

Singing for the lonely
We're not the only ones who feel this
So scared of what I'm doing
All the time

Singing for the Lonely
We're not the only ones who feel this
Scared of what we're doing
All the time

Better Man

Send someone to love me
I need to rest in arms
Keep me safe from harm
In pouring rain

Give me endless summer
Lord I fear the cold
Feel I'm getting old
Before my time

As my soul heals the shame
I will grow through this pain
Lord I'm doing all I can
To be a better man

Go easy on my conscience
'Cause it's not my fault
I know I've been taught
To take the blame

Rest assured my angels
Will catch my tears
Walk me out of here
I'm in pain

As my soul heals the shame
I will grow through this pain
Lord I'm doing all I can
To be a better man

Once you've found that lover
You're homeward bound
Love is all around
Love is all around

I know some have fallen
On stony ground
But Love is all around

Send someone to love me
I need to rest in arms
Keep me safe from harm
In pouring rain

Give me endless summer
Lord I fear the cold
Feel I'm getting old
Before my time

As my soul heals the shame
I will grow through this pain
Lord I'm doin' all I can
To be a better man

Love Calling Earth

This is love calling earth
Do you know how much it hurts?
I didn't die overnight
In the wind I had candlelight
I'm controlled by my fear
All the voices in my head
That I can hear

Please don't hurt me

How do I learn
To give love and be loved in return
If this is heaven I'm falling
I'd rather jump and run away
Than see it burn
I feel I could die
Before I sleep I kiss your cheek
And say goodbye

I'm so sorry
Please don't hurt me

This is love calling earth
Do you know how much it hurts?
I didn't die overnight
In the wind I had candlelight

I'm controlled by my fear
And all the voices in my head
That I can hear

I'm so sorry
Please don't hurt me

If you could see me through my mother's eye
Only then would you begin to realise
All the places I have ever been
Have scared me half to death or
somewhere in-between

I'm so sorry
Please...

Supreme

Oh it seemed forever stopped today
All the lonely hearts in London
Caught a plane and flew away
And all the best women are married
All the handsome men are gay
You feel deprived

Yeah are you questioning your size?
Is there a tumour in your humour,
Are there bags under your eyes?
Do you leave dents where you sit,
Are you getting on a bit?
Will you survive
You must survive

When there's no love in town
This new century keeps bringing you down
All the places you have been
Trying to find a love supreme
A love supreme

Oh what are you really looking for?
Another partner in your life to abuse and to adore?
Is it lovey dovey stuff,
Do you need a bit of rough?
Get on your knees

Yeah turn down the love songs that you hear
'Cause you can't avoid the sentiment
That echoes in your ear
Saying love will stop the pain
Saying love will kill the fear
Do you believe
You must believe
When there's no love in town
This new century keeps bringing you down
All the places you have been
Trying to find a love supreme
A love supreme

I spy with my little eye
Something beginning with (ah)
Got my back up
And now she's screaming so I've got to turn the track up
Sit back and watch the royalties stack up
I know this girl she likes to switch teams
And I'm a fiend but I'm living for a love supreme

When there's no love in town
This new century keeps bringing you down
All the places you have been
Trying to find a love supreme
A love supreme

Come and live a love supreme
Don't let it get you down
Everybody lives for love

Repeat...

The Road To Mandalay

Save me from drowning in the sea
Beat me up on the beach

What a lovely holiday
There's nothing funny left to say

This sombre song would drain the sun
But it won't shine until it's sung

No water running in the stream
The saddest place we've ever been

Everything I touched was golden
Everything I loved got broken
On the road to Mandalay
Every mistake I've ever made
Has been rehashed and then replayed
As I got lost along the way

There's nothing left for you to give
The truth is all that you're left with
Twenty paces then at dawn
We will die and be reborn

I like to sleep beneath the trees
Have the universe at one with me
Look down the barrel of a gun
And feel the Moon replace the Sun

Everything we've ever stolen
Has been lost returned or broken
No more dragons left to slay
Every mistake I've ever made
Has been rehashed and then replayed
As I got lost along the way

Save me from drowning in the sea
Beat me up on the beach
What a lovely holiday
There's nothing funny left to say.

Kids

Me no bubbletious
Me smoke heavy tar
Me be groovin' slowly where you are
Notify your next of kin
'Cause you're never coming back
I've been dropping beats since Back in Black

And we'll paint by numbers
'Til something sticks
Don't mind doing it for the kids
(So come on) jump on board
Take a ride (yeah)
(You'll be doin' it all right)
Jump on board feel the high
'Cause the kids are alright

You've got a reputation
Well I guess that can be explored
You're dancing with the chairman of the board
Take a ride on my twelve cylinder symphony
But if you got other plans
The purpose of a woman is to love her man

And we'll paint by numbers
'Til something sticks
Don't mind doing it for the kids
(So come on) jump on board
Take a ride (yeah)
(Doin' it all right)
Jump on board feel the high
'Cause the kids are alright

I'm gonna give it all of my loving
It's gonna take up all of my love
I'm gonna give it all of my loving
It's gonna take up all of my love
I'm gonna give it all of my loving
It's gonna take up all of my love
I'm gonna give it all of my loving
It's gonna take up all of my love

Come down from the ceiling
I didn't mean to get so high
I couldn't do what I wanted to do
When my lips were dry
You can't just up and leave me
I'm a singer in a band
Well I like drummers baby
You're not my bag

Jump on board
Take a ride, yeah
(You'll be doin' it all right)
Jump on board feel the high, yeah

Jump on board
Take a ride, yeah
(You'll be doin' it all right)
Jump on board feel the high, yeah

I'm an honorary Sean Connery, born '74
There's only one of me
Single-handedly raising the economy
Ain't no chance of the record company dropping me
Press be asking do I care for sodomy
I don't know, yeah, probably
I've been looking for serial monogamy
Not some bird that looks like Billy Connolly
But for now I'm down for ornithology
Grab your binoculars, come follow me

If It's Hurting You

Please don't think of me
If you do you gotta block it
I got chills tonight
And you can't be here to stop it
I'm not a parasite
It's just a lonely night
Tonight

I walked from the bar
'Cause they were only laughing
I wished on our star
But they covered it in satin
I'm not a gigolo
That's what I want you to know
Tonight

Ooh ooh
I've hurt you I can see
Ooh ooh
Do you think it's not hurting me

Ooh ooh
The grass ain't always green
And if it's hurting you
You know that's its hurting me
You know that's its hurting me

You'll meet other men
Who will break your heart
If I see you with them
It's gonna tear me apart

Maybe in another life
We wouldn't be alone
Tonight

Ooh ooh
I've hurt you I can see
Ooh ooh
Do you think its not hurting me

Ooh ooh
The grass ain't always green
And if it's hurting you
You know that it's hurting me
You know that it's hurting me
You know that it's hurting me
You know that it's hurting me

Forever Texas

First you say you want me
Then you don't want me really
Baby do I scare you
Am I talkin' too freely

I got no perspective
On the things that you lack
Baby I don't care
Just lie on your back

Baby I'm crazy
But lady I'm lazy
Amaze me
Baby I'm fading
My mind's all jaded
Amaze me

I'm so superstitious
So there's something you should know
The reason I'm doing you is
'Cause your friend said 'no'

I've been suicidal since
God I don't know when
So get down on your knees
Say your prayers Amen

Baby I'm crazy
Lady I'm lazy
Amaze me
Baby I'm faded
My mind's all jaded

Give me Texas wisdom
Massive systems
And a luscious behind
Mother said 'Son if you do
it too long you'll go blind'

Baby I'm lazy
But lady I'm crazy
Amaze me
Baby I'm faded
My mind's all jaded
One, two

Everybody getting cash for the bung
Everybody wants to know how I'm hung
You can read it in the papers
I'm a giver not a taker
But it won't be the same

Repeat...

Knutsford City Limits

You said I was northern scum
I was wounded baby
That's fighting talk where I'm from
And I'm not moving baby
Spent my life dancing with shadows in strobe lights
It's alright, everything mellows in sunlight

And now London's got its gimmicks
And New York's had its minute
But Knutsford City limits
I'll never change

I've been running nearly all my life
It left me broken baby
When the meter ran out on life
I used my tokens lady
Spent my life dancing with shadows in strobe lights
Now it's alright, everything mellows in sunlight

And now London's got its gimmicks
And New York's had its minute
But Knutsford City limits
I'll never change

London's got its gimmicks
And New York's had its minute
But Knutsford City limits
I'll never change

I've been running nearly all my life
It left me broken baby
When the meter ran out on life
I used my tokens lady
You said I was Northern scum
I was wounded baby
That's fighting talk where I'm from
And I'm not moving baby

London's got its gimmicks
And New York's had its minute
But Knutsford City limits
I'll never change

Saw one transmission
On the television
Saying I can't do my job
Well I just kept dancing
Don't hate me 'cause I'm handsome
And the beat will never stop

Repeat...

By All Means Necessary

Canned laughter for applause
You've opened doors
In and out of their wives
In and out of your smalls
It's not a BAFTA you're after
You want a million dollar lay
By all means necessary
You will get your way

It all seems so easy
But so are you
That's what I've heard them say

All the make up that you wear
Can't hide the flaws
Your work in charity for your own cause
You won't be dating a teacher
You'd rather shag a manic street preacher
By all means necessary
You will get your way

It all seems so easy
But so are you
That's what I've heard them say

Sex with a stranger
You've been laid in a manger
And you think he's your saviour
Will he leave his pager?
You could be his daughter
Look what he's bought ya
But the money won't change ya
Of that there's no danger
Now your life's gettin' darker
It's you that they're after
Fifteen minutes a martyr
Blame it on your father
That dress nearly fits ya
Girl what's possessed you
Can we please take your picture
You know they'll forget ya
Ooh yeah

It all seems so easy
But so are you
That's what I've heard them say

By all means necessary
You will get your way
By all means necessary
You will get your way
By all means necessary
You will get your way

You don't get your way
By giving it away

Repeat...

Let Love Be Your Energy

Words and Music by
Robert Williams and Guy Chambers

(Let love be your energy.)

Yeah.

Well, if you want it, come and make a stance,— so when it's in your hands,— peo-ple show— me love.—

Well, if you want it, come and make a stance,— so when it's in your hands,— peo-ple show— me love.—

Better Man

Words and Music by
Robert Williams and Guy Chambers

Rock DJ

Words and Music by
Robert Williams, Guy Chambers, Kelvin Andrews,
Nelson Pigford and Ekundayo Paris

(1.) Me with the floor-show, kick-in' with your tor-so. Boys get-ting high and the girls ev-en more so.
(2.) Sing-in' in the class-es, mu-sic for your mass-es. Give no head, no back-stage pass-es.

Wave your hands if you're not with the man. Can I kick it? (Yes you can.—)
Have a pro-per gig-gle, I'll be quite po-lite. But when I rock the mike, I rock the mike. (Right.) You

Supreme

Words and Music by
Robert Williams, Guy Chambers, Dino Fekaris
and Frederick Perren

Spoken: I   spy   with my   lit - tle eye

some - thing be - gin - ning with. (ah)   Got my back up   and now she's scream-ing so I've got to turn the track up.

Kids

Words and Music by
Robert Williams and Guy Chambers

If It's Hurting You

Words and Music by
Robert Williams and Guy Chambers

Please don't think of me,   if you do you got-ta block it.
I walked from the bar   'cause they were on-ly laugh-ing.
You'll meet oth-er men   who will break your heart.

I got chills to-night   and you can't be here to stop it.
I wished on our star   but they cov-ered it in sa-tin.
If I see you with them   it's gon-na tear me a-part.

I'm not a pa-ra-site, / it's just a lone-ly night___ to-night.___
I'm not a gi-go - lo. / That's what I want you to know___ to-night.___
May-be in an-oth-er life / we would-n't be a - lone to-night.

Ooh,___ ooh.___ I've hurt you, I___ can see.___

Ooh,___ ooh.___

Singing For The Lonely

Words and Music by
Robert Williams and Guy Chambers

Love Calling Earth

Words and Music by
Kelvin Andrews, Robert Williams
and Guy Chambers

Knutsford City Limits

Words and Music by
Robert Williams, Guy Chambers
and Kelvin Andrews

Forever Texas

Words and Music by
Robert Williams and Guy Chambers

(1.) First you say you want me, then you don't want me real - ly. Ba - by do I scare you? Am I
(2.) I'm so su - per - sti - tious, so there's some - thing you should know. The rea - son I'm do - ing you is 'cause your

Ooh ooh, ooh ooh ooh,— ooh ooh ooh.—

By All Means Necessary

Words and Music by
Robert Williams and Guy Chambers

(1.) Canned laugh-ter___ for ap-plause, you've op-ened___ doors.___
(2.) All the make-up___ that you wear can't hide the flaws.___

In and out of their wives,___ in and out of your
Your work in cha-ri-ty___ for your own

The Road To Mandalay

Words and Music by
Robert Williams and Guy Chambers

Verse lyrics:
1. Save me from drown-ing in the sea, beat me up on the beach.
2. This som-bre song would drain the sun, but it won't shine un-til it's sung.

What a love-ly ho-li-day, there's noth-ing fun-ny left to say.
No wa-ter run-ning in the stream, the sad-dest place we've ev-er been.